ONCE UPON A STEM

H... and ...el

Written by **Robin** ...rated by **Amy Li**

BookLife
PUBLISHING

©2021
BookLife Publishing Ltd.
King's Lynn
Norfolk, PE30 4LS

ISBN: 978-1-83927-168-7

Written by:
Robin Twiddy

Edited by:
Emilie Dufresne

Designed by:
Amy Li

A catalogue record for this book is available from the British Library.

All facts, statistics, web addresses and URLs in this book were verified as valid and accurate at time of writing. No responsibility for any changes to external websites or references can be accepted by either the author or publisher.

All rights reserved. Printed in Malaysia.

Words that look like this can be found in the glossary on page 24.

Photo credits

All images are courtesy of Shutterstock.com, unless otherwise specified. With thanks to Getty Images, Thinkstock Photo and iStockphoto. Recurring images (cover and internal) – artcreator (Professor), Yamabika, The_Pixel, MoonRock (paper textures), kotoffei, Venomous Vector, illustrator096 (decorative vectors), p2–3 – Pretty Vectors, Tori20, p8–9 – Ikstock, Graphiteska, p16–17 – Svetlana Prokhorova, p18–19 – Mironova Iuliia, elenabsl, Mountain Brothers, phoelixD, Yevgenij_D, p22–23 – Ikstock, hendria.

Professor Everafter's lab, around bedtime...

Welcome, I am Professor Everafter and I really like STEM subjects. These are science, technology, engineering and mathematics.

Hansel and Gretel

I have been studying these fairy tales but some parts just don't make sense. Maybe I can make them work with my knowledge of STEM subjects!

Once upon a STEM...

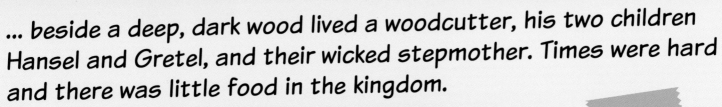

... beside a deep, dark wood lived a woodcutter, his two children Hansel and Gretel, and their wicked stepmother. Times were hard and there was little food in the kingdom.

The deep, dark wood

Why is there always a deep, dark wood?

That night, Hansel and Gretel could hear their stepmother talking through the walls. "We can't feed four mouths. Let's take the children into the forest and leave them there! Then we won't have to feed them as well!" said their stepmother.

Hansel quickly snuck outside and filled his pockets with white stones. He had a plan.

The next morning, their stepmother led them very deep into the woods. Whilst they walked, Hansel dropped the white stones behind him. Their stepmother promised to come back. She never did.

"When the Moon comes out, the stones will shine, showing us the path home," said Hansel.

Now, if Hansel used a phosphorescent paint, then it wouldn't matter if the Moon was shining or not.

This paint has phosphorescent chemicals in it. That means that it 'charges' up in the sunlight. And then will glow when it gets dark.

Phosphorescent just means something that gives off light without heat, making it able to glow in the dark.

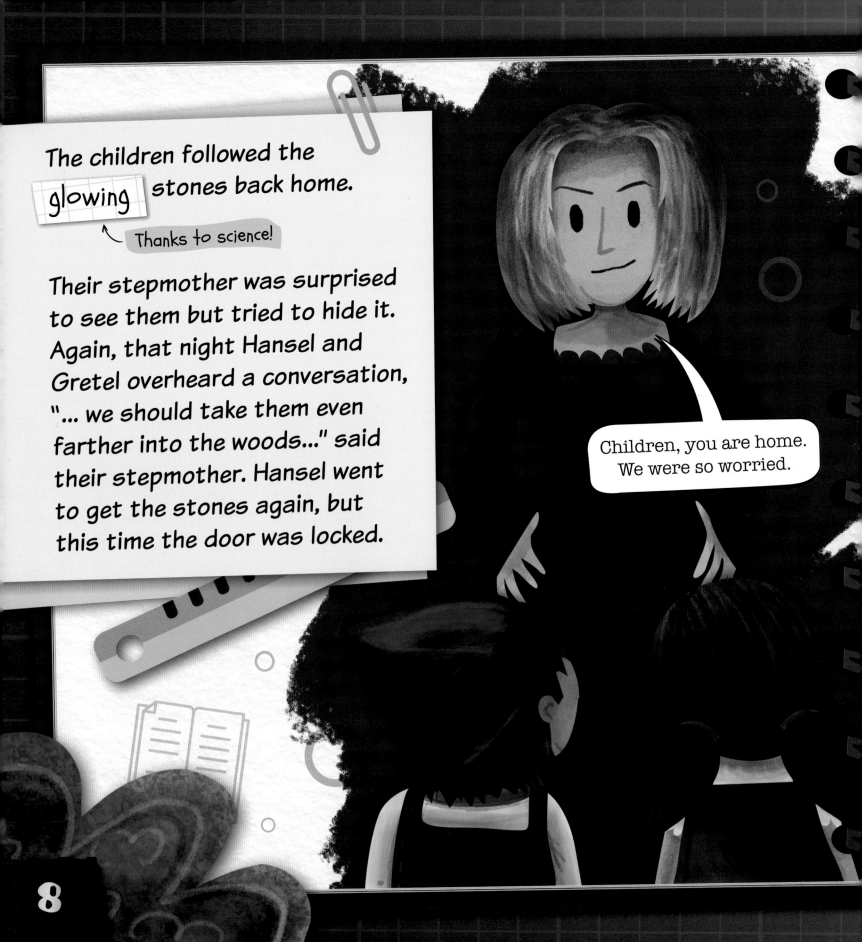

The children followed the glowing stones back home.

↖ Thanks to science!

Their stepmother was surprised to see them but tried to hide it. Again, that night Hansel and Gretel overheard a conversation, "... we should take them even farther into the woods..." said their stepmother. Hansel went to get the stones again, but this time the door was locked.

Children, you are home. We were so worried.

When they set out, their wicked stepmother gave them each some hard, stale bread. Jack had an idea. Because he didn't have the stones to drop and mark their path, he would drop a trail of breadcrumbs instead.

The deep, dark wood

BEWARE!

This time they went even deeper into the deep, dark wood. Again, their wicked stepmother promised to come back for them. Of course, she never did. When the Moon came out, Hansel looked for the breadcrumb trail, but the crumbs had all been eaten by the birds.

Of course, the birds ate the breadcrumbs. They are birds!

Shoo, bird!

Without a trail to follow home, the children soon became lost in the deep, dark wood. They walked for days. Hansel and Gretel had never felt so hungry.

On the third morning of walking through the wood, they came across a clearing.

Before the two very hungry children stood a small <u>cottage</u>. The cottage walls were made from gingerbread and the windows were made of <u>sugar glass</u>. Every part of the cottage was made from something sweet. Hansel's tummy rumbled.

"Come on, Hansel," said Gretel, breaking off a piece of the wall and stuffing it into her mouth. Hansel quickly joined her. They were so hungry that they did not even think about how strange this was.

Tweet!

Wait a minute! A cottage made from gingerbread? It's time to put on my engineer's hat.

A gingerbread house would collapse under its own weight without a <u>frame</u>. Even with a frame made of a strong <u>material</u> such as wood, I <u>estimate</u> that it would still take around 10,000 bricks made of gingerbread to cover a small cottage like this one. Not to mention all that icing to hold it together!

Needs wooden supports here.

Here too!

Prof. Everafter

14

A wooden frame would make the whole __structure__ stronger and stop the weak gingerbread from bending and collapsing under all that weight.

Kids, you should never eat food you find laying around in the woods. Especially if it is someone else's house.

Gulp.

Suddenly an old lady appeared in the doorway. "Come in my dears, I have plenty for you to eat and warm beds for you to sleep in," she said. Little did Hansel and Gretel know, this little old lady was actually a witch who enjoyed eating children.

After the children had eaten their meal, they fell into a deep sleep. While Hansel snoozed, the witch moved him into a cage. When Gretel woke in the morning, she found herself chained to the kitchen. Over the next few weeks, the witch made Gretel do chores and cook lots of food for Hansel.

I like 'em nice and fat. Feed that brother of yours up so I can eat him.

Poor Hansel and Gretel. Take this, you wicked witch!

To gain weight you need to eat more calories than your body uses. If the witch really wanted to make sure that Hansel put on weight, she could have used one of these food tracking apps.

●●●○○ MY MOBILE

85%

Food App 2.0

73%
DAILY CALORIES

	NUTRITIONAL VALUES
Dark chocolate (100 grams)	
One cake slice	505 CALORIES
One apple	183 CALORIES
One burger	43 CALORIES
	292 CALORIES

Not enough calories to fatten up Hansel.

Another piece of technology she could have used would be one of these smart watches. These watches show how much exercise the wearer has done. When we walk, exercise or do anything, we burn calories to give us energy. Any calories we eat but don't use get stored as fat.

Mind you, Hansel probably hasn't done much exercise in that cage.

Weeks later, the witch was finally ready to eat Hansel. "Gretel, can you get inside the oven to see if it has heated up yet?" said the witch, trying to trick Gretel to climb into the oven. But Gretel was smart, so she convinced the witch to climb in herself.

Ha ha ha!

Gretel slammed the oven door shut and locked the witch inside it. She then freed Hansel from the cage. Inside the witch's house, they found precious jewels scattered all around. Hansel and Gretel filled their pockets and set off back into the woods.

Okay, let's do the maths. If Hansel and Gretel needed exactly 100 gold coins to live happily ever after, then how many jewels would they need of each colour? Use the guide to show you how many gold coins the different colours of jewel are worth.

- **Blue jewels = 5** gold coins
- **Red jewels = 10** gold coins

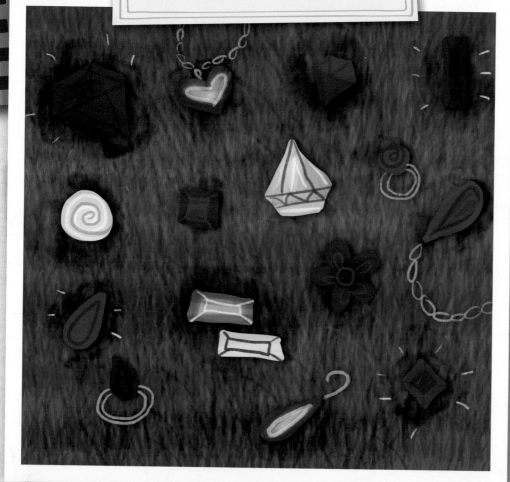

Here are the jewels Hansel and Gretel found. How many do they need to keep?

Answer: 10 red, 0 blue; or 9 red, 2 blue; or 8 red, 4 blue; or 7 red, 6 blue

22

Hansel and Gretel went home to their father, the woodcutter. They found their stepmother had left while they were gone. They showed their father the jewels and they were never poor again. Hansel, Gretel and their father lived happily ever after.

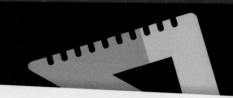

Glossary

apps	applications for a phone or computer that allow it to perform different tasks
calories	things that we use to measure how much energy a food can give your body
chemicals	the things that materials are made from
cottage	a small house usually in the countryside
estimate	make a careful guess
frame	a thing that supports something else
material	a thing from which objects are made
smart watches	a watch that contains a computer which can connect to the internet
structure	a building or shape that is made by connecting different parts
sugar glass	a clear sugar sweet that is see-through and can be eaten

Index